I M

Mac_ _ _eld
The Silk Industry

This young girl is winding pirns also known as quills by hand at Frederick Hall's mill. Between 1875 and 1918 children aged ten could undertake half-time employment on production of a proficiency certificate and could leave school at 13. At this time half timers earned 2/6d (12.5p) per week.

IMAGES OF ENGLAND

Macclesfield
The Silk Industry

Louanne Collins & Moira Stevenson
of
Macclesfield Museums Trust

NONSUCH

Macclesfield from The Common. An engraving of about 1815 showing Roe's windmill and the early industrialisation of the town. Christ Church and the Sunday School are visible on the horizon and the cupola of Roe's Button Mill can also been seen in the middle ground to the right of the large chimney.

First published 1995
This new pocket edition 2006
Images unchanged from first edition

Nonsuch Publishing Limited
The Mill, Brimscombe Port,
Stroud, Gloucestershire, GL5 2QG
www.nonsuch-publishing.com

Nonsuch Publishing is an imprint of Tempus Publishing Group

British Library Cataloguing in Publication Data.
A catalogue record for this book is available from the British Library.

ISBN 1-84588-294-6

Typesetting and origination by Nonsuch Publishing Limited
Printed in Great Britain by Oaklands Book Services Limited

Contents

Weaving shed at J & T Brocklehurst's c. 1910 from a collection of postcards illustrating all the processes undertaken by the firm. The looms in the picture are shaft looms controlled by dobbies and small jacquard looms.

Acknowledgements

The publication of this collection of photographs of the silk industry has been made possible through the generosity of the companies and individuals who gave or loaned the photographs to develop the archive held by the Silk Museum. The names are too numerous to list individually here. In a number of cases the same image has been donated by more than one person.

The Museum Trust would like to thank all the contributors to the archive and it is hoped that this publication will bring pleasure not only to those who have contributed to it, but to everyone who participated or are interested in the silk industry of the town.

Introduction

Macclesfield has associations with silk dating back nearly four hundred years when buttons covered with silk and mohair twist were manufactured in the area. Yarn preparation began in the middle of the 17th century and hand throwing took place in shades, which were long narrow brick built sheds.

Charles Roe established the first water powered throwing mill in Macclesfield in 1744, based on Italian technology brought to England twenty five years earlier by John and Thomas Lombe. Within a short time Macclesfield became a centre of the throwing industry, supplying yarn to the Spitalfield weavers. In the 19th and 20th centuries firms such as William Frost, J & T Brocklehurst and G H Heath were significant silk throwsters supplying yarns to the weaving and knitwear industries throughout Britain.

Whilst the weaving of narrow fabrics and smallwares began in the mid 17th century, broadloom weaving was introduced to the town in the late 18th century, and Macclesfield quickly flourished as a centre for the production of bandannas and the plain lustrous silk in fashion by that time.

The early silk weaving trade was a hand industry carried out in the weavers' three storey cottages, known as garrets. Over six hundred garretted houses are known to have been built and more than two hundred still remain in the town. Evidence of weaving activity still survives in some of the top storeys.

Macclesfield expanded rapidly between 1810 and 1830 when its population increased from 8,743 to 23,129. In 1814 there were 30 mills, by 1840 there were 70. Most of the manufacturers soon found they could control their workers better in the mills and that standards of work were higher. Powerlooms were introduced to the textile industry in about 1820. After initial problems working with silk, power was superceding handloom weaving by the middle of the century.

The diversity of Macclesfield's production by the mid 1800s can be seen from the local firms' exhibits at The Great Exhibition of 1851, which included velvets and satins for ladies, and serges, vestings and sarsenets for men, along with shawls, handkerchiefs, trimmings and furnishing fabric. Dyeing and printing works were established alongside the throwing, weaving and small wares industries.

In 1836 the National School of Design was founded in London. Initially, Macclesfield did not seek government resources for its own design centre, relying on the Useful Knowledge Society, which did encourage design education. The School of Art was founded in 1852, with government support, and became one of the country's leading art schools. A technical school which gave instruction in throwing, weaving, design and construction of the loom was opened in 1886 alongside the Art School. Many of the designers trained in Macclesfield made significant contributions to the industry nationwide.

Photographic evidence does not exist for the early industry and we have to rely on contemporary reports such as the 1832 Royal Commission Committee of Enquiry, local historians and commentators like John Corry and John Prout, a Macclesfield weaver, newspapers, census returns, directories and artists' impressions, to give us a picture of the industry.

The Macclesfield silk industry experienced a series of booms and slumps throughout its history, usually caused by factors outside its control. During the Napoleonic wars the industry boomed, but on its conclusion Britain lost its American and European markets to France and Italy who could produce high quality goods at a cheaper price. The Free Trade policy adopted by the government in 1825 brought another depression. The Cobden Treaty with France in 1860 finally removed trade barriers, thus allowing the import of cheaper goods, a situation from which the British silk industry never fully recovered.

Emigration was encouraged to the colonies and particularly to Patterson, New Jersey which had become the centre of the American silk industry, founded by John Ryle, a Macclesfield man. Links between Macclesfield and Patterson continue to this day and the descendants of these early immigrants regularly visit Macclesfield searching for their roots.

The earliest photographs of the Macclesfield silk industry show the products included in an exhibition at the Macclesfield School of Art in 1895, when the Duchess of Teck, patron of the silk industry, visited Macclesfield. The exhibits included a wide range of products suitable for female dress, as well as gents' tie silks, mufflers and printed foulards.

Man-made fibres were woven in Macclesfield from about 1900. Comte Hilaire de Chardonnet, who had launched the first successful nitro-cellulose rayon at the Paris exhibition of 1889, worked at Langley with William Whiston when he was printing onto artificial silk in 1815. By the 1920s artificial silk fabrics were being woven and printed alongside silk and gradually superceded the production of silk. Macclesfield firms worked with the chemical manufacturers to produce new man-made fabrics and have always been innovative and adaptable to the new processes and techniques required.

During the Second World War Macclesfield became the centre for the supply of silk, and the silk firms were all engaged in war work, weaving parachute silk, manufacturing silk underwear for airmen and for jungle warfare and producing the now famous 'escape' maps.

Prior to the introduction of water powered throwing, silk was thrown by hand in small low buildings known as shades. Water powered throwing mills, based on the Italian model, were introduced into England in 1718, but hand throwing seems to have continued up to the 20th century in certain areas.

Today, the Macclesfield textile industry has contracted to a fraction of its former size, but firms are still engaged in yarn processing, knitting, dyeing, weaving and printing for both the club tie trade and fashion market here and abroad.

The silk industry dominated the life of the town for over 200 years and influenced all aspects of work and play. The photographs in this book record aspects of this activity and influence over the last 100 years and draw on non-photographic images for the earlier period.

Preserving the Heritage of the Industry

The idea for preserving the history and heritage of the silk industry dates back to the 19th century, and at various points from the 1940s interest was expressed in establishing a museum of the silk industry. During the early 1970s the Borough Librarian had collected material related to the industry and there had even been a budget for the establishment of a museum.

However, none of these attempts materialised, and it was not until 1979, when a Manpower Services Commission STEP Scheme [sponsored by Macclesfield Borough Council, Cheshire County Council and Quarry Bank Mill Styal] was established, that the momentum for the present museum began.

The Manpower Services Commission schemes of the 1970s and 1980s gave the opportunity and resources which helped to realise the ideas. The Friends of Macclesfield Silk Heritage was established in 1980, grew to a membership of approaching five hundred, and was very active in raising money for, and promoting the development of, the Museum. The Macclesfield Sunday School [a Grade II Star listed building] became the home of the Silk Museum which is managed by The Sunday School Heritage Centre Trust, a tripartite body originally made up of representatives of Macclesfield Borough Council, the Friends of Macclesfield Silk Heritage and the former Sunday School Trustees, the latter subsequently replaced by representatives from the wider community. During the period 1981 to 1987 the Sunday School Heritage Centre Trust, with the support of the Friends of Macclesfield Silk Heritage, was responsible for establishing the Silk Museum in the Sunday School building, together with the library, Victorian schoolroom and other educational facilities. In addition they restored the top floor of Paradise Mill, where 26 hand jacquard looms had survived in their original location. Paradise Mill had been owned by the firm of Cartwright and Sheldon who operated in the mill from 1912 and the hand looms had survived with the firm for over seventy years. The looms were restored to working order by the Trust and opened as the first phase of the Silk Museum development in 1984. The Silk Museum was formally opened by the Duchess of Gloucester in 1987 when the Sunday School was fully restored.

Since that time the Macclesfield Museums Trust, which was established in 1987 and is made up of representatives from Macclesfield Borough Council, Cheshire County Council and the Macclesfield Sunday School Heritage Centre Trust, has been responsible for managing and developing museum services in Macclesfield. The Trust has continued to develop the collections related to the silk industry and offers a wide range of education services to support the teaching of the National Curriculum.

The Collections

The photographs in this book have largely been drawn from Macclesfield Museum's photographic archive of over 20,000 images relating to Macclesfield and to the silk industry. The archive was started in 1982 under the auspices of the Macclesfield Sunday School Heritage Centre Silk Museum project and continued by the Macclesfield Museums Trust which was formed in 1987. Macclesfield Museums are extremely grateful to all those who have lent and donated photographs so that this invaluable archive could exist. Local firms have also been

View of 108 Steps, Macclesfield, as portrayed in the woven silk picture which was produced by James Arnold, Tie Specialities Ltd.

generous over the years in allowing their premises and processes to be photographed, thus keeping the archive up to date.

Macclesfield had a number of photographers whose work appeared in postcard format. The best known were Bullock & Sons, who started in Macclesfield and later opened premises in Congleton and Stockport. Other local photographers included are Robert Hughes, F Buckley, R Leech, R White and J Albinson. The Museum has been fortunate to acquire the postcard collection of the late Gordon Campbell, which features the work of these photographers, and images from this collection are included in the publication.

The archive is part of the museum's reference collection of both primary and secondary material. Other aspects of the collections include a survey of the 120 mills and dyehouses of Macclesfield, the research files of the East Cheshire Mill Survey, a survey of the 600 garret houses and the town's churches and Sunday Schools.

There are over three hundred oral history tapes of interviews with former silk workers which have been transcribed and indexed. These can be used in conjunction with the index to the Macclesfield Courier and Herald. The museum holds a near complete run of this local paper from its first issue in 1811 up to the 1970s.

The museum holds the pattern books for Brocklehurst Fabrics, which incorporates J & T Brocklehurst and the Langley Printworks, The Macclesfield Silk Manufacturers Society, Barracks Printing Company, John Godwin & Son (Commercial Designers) and single volumes and short runs from other firms. In 1993 a grant from the Pilgrim Trust enabled the museum to undertake a survey of the silk manufacturers' pattern books held in both public and private hands. The results of the survey can be studied in the museum. A book based on the survey: Silk, Satins, Sarsenets, Steels and Stripes was published in 1994.

The Heritage Centre houses a reference library of books and journals relating to costume, textiles and local history. The library and archive may be consulted by members of the public by appointment with the museum curator.

One

Housing the Industry

Macclesfield's landscape has been dominated by the industrial architecture of the textile industry. One hundred and twenty mills and dye houses were erected in the town between 1740 and 1940. Roe's Button Mill, built in 1744, was the first of a number of water powered throwing mills and the start of the factory system in Macclesfield. The majority of mills were built in the early 19th century in a variety of styles. Now less than half are still standing and are mainly converted to small factory units for other uses.

There is evidence that the horse gin and water wheel were both used to power cotton spinning mules in the town. The development of steam power technology speeded up the industrialisation of the textile industry, and gas engines were installed in some mills before electrification.

Over 600 garreted houses were built in the town, mainly erected by the mill architects. The houses were sometimes built in rows with a long attic running across a number of properties and having a separate external stair. These were often owned by silk manufacturers who rented out loom space. In other examples each house was a self-contained unit with access from the domestic floors to the attic by ladder. The whole family would have been involved in the silk processes. An outstanding and unusual example of a double garret, the building having four storeys, is 56-58 Mill Lane which was built in the early 19th century.Many other houses also have evidence of weaving still apparent in the attics, although most have now been converted for modern day living.

Surviving photographs, a selection of which are included in this publication, show how the development of Macclesfield has been influenced by the rise and decline of the silk industry.

Print of Macclesfield viewed from The Hollins c. 1850 showing the extent of the mills and mill ponds built to accommodate and power the industry.

Above: The Button Mill (right) was built in 1744 by Charles Roe and was the first mill in Macclesfield. It housed the first water powered silk throwing machinery in the town. This technology was first used in England at Derby by John and Thomas Lombe. The Royal Depot Mill (left) built in 1815 served for a time as an assessment office for the return of duties paid on raw silk.

Left: A portrait of Charles Roe by Wright of Derby. Roe, although initially involved in silk, also had a copper works in Macclesfield using copper from Alderley Edge, Coniston and Anglesey. Trade tokens known as Macclesfield pennies and halfpennies were minted for him in Birmingham and Liverpool between 1789 and 1791.

This aerial view of Pickford Street, with Pickford St Mills and Wood St Mill, highlights what Macclesfield must have looked like in the 1950s when there were 120 mills integrated with domestic and commercial properties in the centre of the town.

This view of Pickford Street, taken in 1995, shows how the area has drastically changed with the Normid Superstore and car park where Pickford St Mills once stood. On the left side of Pickford Street are the boarded up windows of Wood Street Mill, empty since the closure of James Arnold & Co in 1993.

Above: Thorp Street Gas Mill built in 1827, was reduced to three storeys after a fire in 1977. It was originally used for silk throwing and later smallware and trimming manufacture. Between 1913 and 1977 the business was owned by Berisfords of Congleton. The building has subsequently been converted to a variety of other textile uses.

Opposite above: The Park Green Mill complex, when occupied by William Frost, Silk Throwster, was very extensive, as this aerial view shows. In the late 1970s a fire severely damaged the Mill Lane wing, which was subsequently reduced in height. The machinery was originally powered by water. The mill clock, which was linked to production, recorded mill time and real time, and is now in the Museum of Science and Industry, Manchester.

Opposite below: This bridge over Pickford Street was built in 1920 and connected the mill belonging to G H Heath, Silk Throwsters, with the sorting rooms on the opposite corner.

The Regency Mill, Chester Road, is a fine example of a pedimented mill built in the 1820s. All the processes of silk throwing and silk manufacture, including dyeing, were integrated on the site, and steam power was used to power many of the processes.

VALUABLE FREEHOLD SILK FACTORY & PROPERTY,

IN CHESTERGATE AND KING EDWARD STREET, MACCLESFIELD.

TO BE SOLD BY AUCTION,

BY MR. KNIGHT,

AT THE "ANGEL INN," MACCLESFIELD,

ON THURSDAY, THE 28th OF JULY, 1859,

AT SEVEN O'CLOCK IN THE EVENING. SUBJECT TO SUCH CONDITIONS AS SHALL BE THEN PRODUCED:

LOT 1---ALL THAT

SILK FACTORY

WAREHOUSE, AND PREMISES,

Fronting to Chestergate, and extending into King Edward Street, in Macclesfield aforesaid, being three stories high, and now, or late in the occupation of Peter Moll and Co., Mr. Thomas Wheelton, and Mr. William Davenport.

LOT 2.--ALL THOSE FIVE

Messuages, or Dwelling-Houses & Shops,

Fronting to King Edward Street aforesaid, and adjoining Lot 1, together with the Yard, Outoffices, and premises, now in the respective occupations of James Smith, Thomas Wadsworth, Mary Ann Smith, and Elizabeth Longshaw.

This Property is Freehold of Inheritance, and is in an excellent situation. There is a well in the yard belonging to the Factory, capable of supplying a steam engine with water. The Houses are modern and very substantially built.

For further particulars apply to Mr. James Dewhurst, the Owner; or to the Auctioneer, or at the offices of Messrs. Parrott, Colville, and May, Solicitors, Macclesfield.

M. BURGESS, PRINTER, MARKET PLACE, MACCLESFIELD.

The silk industry was particularly vulnerable to fluctuations in trade. It thrived in times of prosperity when there was a great demand for luxury products. The industry was protected from foreign competition by import tariffs, which were removed in phases up to the introduction of Free Trade in 1860. After this time the British silk industry found it hard to compete with cheaper foreign imports and many firms went bankrupt.

Cartwright and Sheldon built Vincent St Mill as a silk weaving shed in 1919 to house fifty jacquard powerlooms on the ground floor and twenty Ruti looms in the basement. Extensions were added in the 1930s and 1950s. The mill closed in 1978 and the premises were later bought by Michael Twigg Joinery.

Weaving sheds to accommodate power looms were usually single storey structures with maximum use of roof lighting. This interior view of Vincent Street Mill demonstrates the use of steel roof structures, which illuminates the need for the supporting cast iron columns required by the timber roof structures of the earlier mills.

Paradise Street garret houses after restoration show the original narrow windows at second floor level, which maximised the day light necessary for the skilled work of the hand loom weaver. Over 600 garret properties were built in the town, of which over 200 still survive and make attractive modern homes.

Pitt Street c. 1960 showing a terrace of garret properties. The working area would have been accessed from the first floor living quarters by a narrow ladder to the attic where weaving and related activities took place.

Above: The outside staircase to the weavers' garrets in Chapel Street gave independent access to the weaving floor, which was not accessible from the houses below. James Arnold & Co employed six weavers who continued hand weaving on the premises until the 1950s. Products included altar cloths and reppe weave stripes.

Left: One of the six weavers in the Chapel Street garret who is probably weaving reppe stripe material on a shaft loom. Women often worked as weavers on shaft looms, but the heavier work of jacquard weaving was usually undertaken by men.

Mr Fred Booth with Miss Polly Walker at 16 Statham Street in 1928. The looms came from Cartwright and Sheldon and were returned to Paradise Mill in the 1940s when Mr Booth retired.

Line drawing from Alfred Barlow's History of Weaving, published 1878. Details of the garret include the trap door access, typical small paned windows and canaries. Whilst male members of the family undertook the majority of the weaving, the women and children were employed with other tasks such as winding the pirns.

Two

Yarn Preparation

Charles Roe established the first water powered throwing mill in Macclesfield in 1744 and the industry developed rapidly. Initially, the Macclesfield throwsters prepared yarn for the Spitalfields weavers, and after about 1780 for the local market.

The throwsters enjoyed a relatively high level of prosperity for a century but then suffered from the free trade principles of 1860. Silk throwsters of note in Macclesfield in the 19th and up to the middle of the 20th century include J & T Brocklehursts, William Frost and G H Heath.

In spite of the general commercial difficulties in the silk industry at that time, Ernest Scragg, throwing machinery makers, was founded in 1889. The invention of rayon and other man made fibres gave a boost to the industry and the development of nylon in the latter half of the last century has been particularly important. The processes known as yarn texturing were developed in the 1950s and today Mowbrays, founded in 1928, textures nylon for the production of items such as stockings, socks and lace. F Harding & Co, founded in 1949, process synthetic yarns for a wide range of industrial uses and export world wide.

Engraving of silk winding from *The Manufacture of Silk* published c. 1860.

Above: This photograph, lent by Paul Anderton, is from a collection of 1930s images in the Leek Heritage Archive. Hand throwing of silk survived in Leek until the 1940s.

Left: Before World War II much of the raw silk came from Japan. During the war the Silk and Rayon Control, with its headquarters in Macclesfield, had to procure silk from other sources. Peter Gaddum and Eric Whiston travelled extensively in the Middle East to secure supplies to support the war effort.

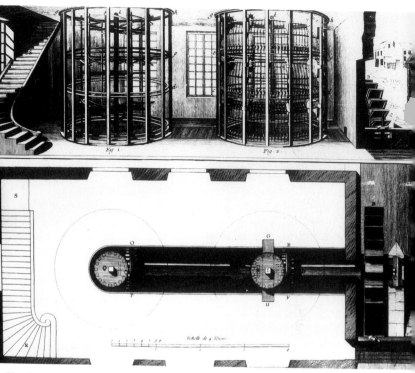

The illustration shows the water powered drive to the silk throwing machinery, which was developed in the Piedmont region of Northern Italy in the 15th century, and brought to England by John and Thomas Lombe of Derby in 1718. This illustration is from the *L'Encylopedie Diderot et d'Alemert*.

Silk bale room at G H Heath's in 1933. The silk was imported in woven protective sacks and was stored in the basement where the slightly damp conditions suited the fibre.

Despatch room at G H Heath's in 1933. Here thrown silk wound onto cones or made into hanks or skeins was weighed and packed into wooden crates for despatch all over the country.

Silk throwing at J & T Brocklehurst's c. 1910. Throwing is the process which imparts twist into the yarn. The number of threads and amount of twist determines the properties of the yarn and gives it characteristics required for different end uses. Here, women and children provide the bulk of the workforce, with men acting as supervisors. The children pictured here would probably have been half-timers attending school for part of each day.

Skein to bobbin winding c. 1920. Silk throwing involved a number of processes which involved winding, doubling and throwing. This would involve transferring the form of the yarn from skeins to bobbins and bobbin to bobbin, depending on the process and the form required. Here, silk is being taken from the skein form and wound onto the bobbin. The skeins are held on 'swifts' which support the skein while it is being wound off.

ENOCH RUSHTON,

Millwright, Engineer,

SILK MACHINIST,

AND

GENERAL MILL FURNISHER,

ROYAL DEPOT & DUKE STREET MILLS,

MACCLESFIELD.

STEEL RODS & CLEANER KNIVES SUPPLIED.

Steam Guages, Lubricators, India Rubbers, Screws, Bolts, &c.

ALL KINDS OF IMPROVED GUIDER MOTIONS.

PATENTEE OF THE SELF-ACTING COUNT AND REGISTER AND TAKE

The firm of Enoch Rushton was established in 1855 as silk machinists, engineers and mill finishers with premises at the Royal Depot Mills and Duke Street Mill. Starting in a small way they later supplied machinery to silk manufacturers throughout Britain.

Enoch Rushton & Sons later moved their works to Davenport Street where they specialised in manufacturing winding, reeling, doubling, warping and beaming machinery. The firm won a gold medal at the 1873 London Exhibition. They also supplied wooden accessories such as swifts.

28

An advertisement for Enoch Rushton and Sons from the Silk Journal and Rayon World of 1929. The advertisement gives details of the range of machinery supplied by the firm.

Advertisement from Silk Journal and Rayon World 1930. Ernest Scragg and Sons Ltd, who also manufactured machinery for both silk and man made fibres, was founded in 1889. Reiter-Scragg, with its headquarters in Langley, continues the tradition of manufacturing throwing machinery and exports all over the world.

Ring spinning, also known as ring doubling or ring twisting, at Williams Frost's Mill in 1933. William Frost's had been engaged in throwing since 1858 and purchased Park Green Mills from W H Eaton in 1881. Together with Heath's they processed the first Coventry produced rayon and were the first to set up a department exclusively for processing rayon yarn.

Silk winding at J & T Brocklehurst *c.* 1910. Silk was wound from bobbins onto skeins before being sent out for dyeing. The machines in use were probably produced by Enoch Rushton & Sons.

Doubling and lacing at William Frost's Mill in 1933. This building was in the centre of the Park Green Mills complex and was demolished after the fire in 1976. To the right of the image women are engaged in lacing, which is threading a cord at intervals in the skein to help keep it from getting tangled up during the dyeing processes.

Above: Throwing at Brocklehurst Whiston Amalgamated in 1933. This machine is putting a high degree of twist into a single thread. Note the line shafting for the belt driven machinery which is closely packed together.

Left: A modern throwing machine at G H Heath & Company in the 1960s used for man made and synthetic fibres. The firm, established in 1876, had two five storey factories and one of four storeys in Macclesfield, an extensive mill in Sandbach and an associated company in Middlewich specialising in crepe yarn. They employed over 1,000 operatives and were the largest firm engaged solely in throwing.

Damaged cocoons and the waste from silk reeling and throwing can also be made into yarn. There is evidence of silk waste spinning in Britain from 1671 and a water powered mill for spinning silk waste was built at Galgate near Lancaster in 1792. J & T Brocklehurst were short staple spinners from about 1820 and long staple spinners from about 1840. The silk came into the country in compact bales and frequently a pick axe was used to break open the bale.

The silk waste is then treated by boiling and degumming. The series of photographs illustrated here were taken between 1910 and 1920.

The dressed silk is spread prior to combing. Initially, the short staple spinning process was employed for spinning silk waste. This involved cutting up the silk waste into lengths of one - two inches (25-50cm) and then using spinning techniques similar to cotton. This resulted in the spun yarn losing the lustrous properties so characteristic of silk.

The silk waste is then combed to align all the fibres prior to the drawing and spinning process. Long staple spinning, using fibres up to ten inches long, was developed by a number of companies. Gibson and Campbell of Glasgow were granted a patent in 1836, but its claims were invalidated since it was said that long staple spinning of silk waste had been practised before. Gibson and Campbell became insolvent in 1840 and J & T Brocklehurst came to their rescue and thus acquired the use of the process.

The fibre is drawn out to produce a sliver. This is a soft rope of parallel fibres which can be drawn out further and twisted. Silk waste was often mixed with other fibres like wool, alpaca and cashmere. Samuel Lister of Bradford perfected long staple spinning of silk and mixed fibre in the 1850s and Bradford became the centre for mixed fibre spinning.

The soft rope is drawn out further to create the appropriate thickness prior to spinning. A further development of spinning silk waste came in the late 1870s when Thomas Wardle of Leek introduced tussah or wild silk to Britain.

After all the preparatory stages the waste silk is finally ready for spinning. The spinning process imparts twist which binds the parallel fibres together and gives the yarn strength.

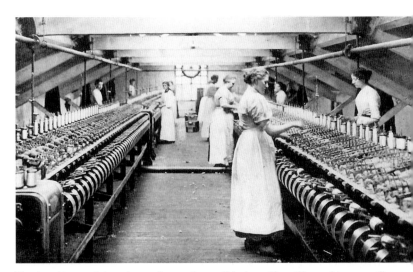

The thread is passed through a gas flame to burn off the loose fibres. The resulting spun silk yarn has different properties to the filament yarn and while the fibre still takes colour well it lacks the lustre of filament yarn. There were nine spinning mills left in Britain after the Second World War, including one in Macclesfield, but by 1971 they had all closed.

Three

Design and Designers

Design has always been seen as a vital element in the silk industry since it could provide commercial advantage over competitors. It was the competition with the standards of design in Europe, and particularly in France, that caused the government to provide funds to support colleges of art and design in Britain in the 1830s and 1840s. Macclesfield did not take advantage of this support until 1852, since local manufacturers seemed content with the instruction provided in drawing by the Useful Knowledge Society. The Art School, established over the Useful Knowledge Society's premises in Park Green, moved to new purpose built premises in Park Lane in 1879. The earliest reference to textile designers in Macclesfield appears in the census of 1841. Throughout their apprenticeship designers were expected to attend day release classes at the Art School. Designers usually specialised in either jacquard or print design. In the early years the designers appeared to be exclusively men, but in the 20th century women joined the profession, particularly in the field of print design.

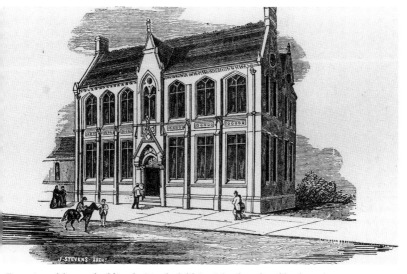

Engraving of the new building for Macclesfield Art School produced by the architect J Stephens in 1879. Designers who trained at the Art School were employed in Macclesfield and in the silk industry nationally.

Above: James Walmsley designed for block printing at the BWA Langley Printworks. He is seen here finishing the design for a corner block in 1948. Corner blocks were introduced to save time in printing.

Left: The finished corner block is examined for flaws. The artistic design has now been transferred to the block ready for printing.

Lesley Robinson and colleagues working in Paradise Mill at the Cartwright and Sheldon design studio in 1933. Note the adjustable lights over the sloping drafting tables.

This City and Guilds Silver medal was awarded to William Rothwell in 1906 (left). Prizes were awarded for both design and technical expertise.

William B Wright was awarded the Owen Jones Competition medal in 1910 (right). Macclesfield students had a high reputation throughout the country.

Bill Hine joined B.W.A aged fifteen and served a five year apprenticeship as a jacquard designer. He worked at BWA throughout his career, rising to head designer before he retired in the 1970s. He is seen working on the draft for the 'Sailing of the Mayflower', produced in 1969.

The Sailing of the Mayflower, a silk picture produced by Brocklehurst Whiston Amalgamated. Silk pictures were produced from 1946 until Brocklehurst Fabrics closed in 1990.

The design department at A W Hewetson's Albion Mill about 1955. The firm specialised in embroidery and the head of department at the time was Isaac Findlow who worked at A W Heweton for over fifty years. Hewetsons placed great emphasis on good design, employing a sizeable design team and purchasing designs from freelance designers.

John Hewetson (left) is seen here with the Swiss mechanics who installed the Schiffli embroidery machines at Hewetson's in 1905, seven years after Augustus William Hewetson had founded the firm as a silk embroidery manufacturer.

Designs for biased scarves and handkerchiefs, as seen in the Barracks Printing Co design studio, were popular in 1933 when this photograph was taken. The firm is now essentially a commission printer working for internationally known companies and is part of the Courtaulds Group

Sue Magee (standing left) today heads the print design team at Barracks. The major part of the work of the Barracks studio is developing and adapting customers' ideas to make them suitable for printing.

Four

Woven Fabric Production

Broadloom weaving developed in Macclesfield towards the end of the 18th century and the industry quickly flourished. Originally it was a handwork industry carried out in the workers' three storey houses, known as garrets. Between 1800 and 1830 there was a massive increase in the building of mills, and weavers were soon drawn into the factory system. Macclesfield manufacturers introduced the jacquard mechanism in the 1820s and experimented with powerloom weaving at the same time. In the 19th century hand and power weaving with jacquard, swivel and dobby looms could be found in Macclesfield. Handloom weaving continued until 1981 when the last handloom weaver retired with the closure of Cartwright and Sheldon. In the 20th century firms adapted their machinery to weave artificial silk and invested in rapier shuttleless looms and computerised programs to replace the jacquard mechanism.

The weaving industry spawned a variety of skills and activities. These included the tackler, who built and maintained the looms, the harness builder, the warper and enterers, who prepared the warp and weft ready for weaving, the designer, the card cutter and the mill engineer.

The majority of silk workers were women and Macclesfield was always known as a "women's town". However, the supervisory and 'skilled' jobs were reserved for men, who were usually paid more. The only skilled positions available to women were warping, entering and powerloom weaving.

Etching of a handloom weaver by R A Riseley showing the interior of the garret.

The Macclesfield Silk Manufacturing Society was a registered co-operative of local handloom weavers, who specialised in scarves, cut ups and 28" squares. Power looms were installed in 1902 just after this photograph was taken. The firm was a leading manufacturer in the 1920s and 1930s of the Macclesfield Longscarf - a tie cut with the grain of fabric as opposed to the conventional tie which is cut on the bias.

The hand loom weaving floor of Cartwright and Sheldon at Paradise Mill. The firm began business in the Mill in 1912 and the weavers pictured here in 1933 include Jim Garside and Arthur Burke. Many photographs of Macclesfield silk mills were taken in that year that and the photographer has yet to be identified.

Above: One of the 26 jacquard hand looms at Paradise Mill with Jim Clarke weaving in 1978. The looms are now listed and preserved as part of the Macclesfield Silk Museum, which is open to the public.

Opposite: Jim Clarke, who was the last handloom weaver in Macclesfield, retired in 1981 just before the firm of Cartwright & Sheldon ceased trading. Latterly the firm used handweaving only for short runs and for samples.

Above: A shed at David Whitfield's mill in 1933 closely packed with shaft looms, some weaving 'Macclesfield stripe', which was first introduced by Whitfields. Note the unguarded machinery. The supervisors and overlookers were always men whilst women generally had the less skilled jobs.

Opposite above: A powerloom shed in Macclesfield in 1933 showing the belt drive mechanism which powered the looms prior to the installation of independent electric motors. The shaft looms in the foreground are weaving what appears to be 'Macclesfield Stripe', popular in the 1920s and 1930s.

Opposite below: Harold Snape with the gas engine at James Arnold's Wood Street Mill 1957. It powered fifty looms, winding frames, warping mills, sewing and knitting machines and the finishing and box making machinery.

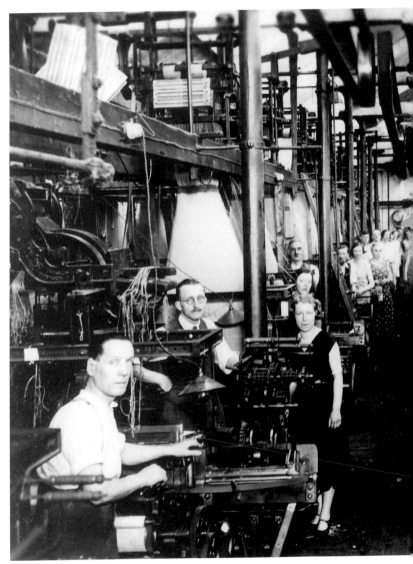

A mixture of shaft looms and power looms with jacquards supported on wooden gantries at T H Hambleton's mill. Hambleton's was established in 1886 and in 1939 was taken over by James Arnold & Co.

The power weaving shed at Brocklehurst Whiston Amalgamated in the late 1930s before the Smith looms were replaced by the faster Ruti looms a few years later.

A Ruti loom at Brocklehurst Whiston Amalgamated in 1948. The cards are placed at the side, as in handlooms, to steady the harness. The original wooden gantries have been replaced by metal.

Above: John Barlow setting up the original looms in Wood Street mill about 1900. The business and premises were acquired by James Arnold & Co in 1913. The original power was 'bought' from the Royal Depot Mill via underground line shafting and it can still be seen in its original position underground..

Opposite: The separate warp beam on this Ruti loom enabled a wider gap (known as the purry) between the harness and beam to lessen stress on the warp threads.

This tackler at Nicholson's in about 1900 is wearing moleskin trousers and a linen jacket, typical garments worn by tacklers. He is carrying his tools known as keys.

Tackler Fred Pyatt working on a Ruti loom. Brocklehurst Whiston Amalgamated replaced their Smith looms with 96 Ruti looms in the late 1930s. The jacquard machine is placed as high up as possible to lessen strain on the harness.

Above: Arthur Eastham is seen here gathering the harness at Paradise Mill in 1985. The looms in the Museum have largely been restored by former silk workers.

Left: Building a jacquard harness on a Ruti loom at Brocklehurst Whiston Amalgamated. Harness building is a skilled and labour intensive job. Great care is needed to ensure accuracy in the tying of knots and measurements of the harness cords.

Gathering the threads in a jacquard harness before entering the harness with the warp, one of the operations needed to prepare a loom for weaving.

Mrs Mathews and Miss S Coop, employees of Brocklehurst Whiston Amalgamated, entering the warp threads through the heddles of a shaft loom.

Entering the warp threads through the reed was a painstaking occupation.

Eric Livesey was one of the last traditional hand twisters to be employed in Macclesfield. Here he is joining the threads of the old warp to those of the new warp on one of the Museum's looms at Paradise Mill. Today this process is done by a knotting machine.

Above: The warping room at J Dunkerley in 1933 with belt driven vertical warp mills. The threads are wound in small sections on to the creel and then on to the warp beam. Warping was one skilled job which was open to women in the silk industry.

Opposite above: A close up showing the section of warp threads passing through the reed. The women are checking for broken ends.

Opposite below: Sizing a warp at Brocklehurst Whiston Amalgamated c. 1948. Sizing the warp gave it strength and made it easier to handle during weaving.

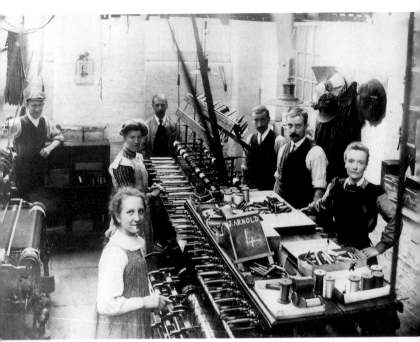

Above: A corner of the weaving shed at Brunswick Mill, Lowe Street, owned by James Arnold & Co, showing a pirn winder. This photograph is one from the collection of family photographs lent to the Museum by Philip Arnold, a member of the Arnold family.

Opposite: The piano cardcutter is cutting the jacquard cards from the point paper design. In Macclesfield the usual number of hooks on the jacquard machine used for the design are 384 or 576. These numbers are easily divisible for various small repeat designs.

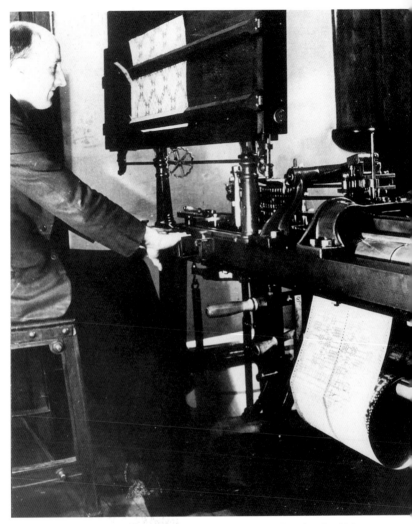

Mr Latham is seen here cutting paper cards which replaced the thick cards at Brocklehurst Whiston Amalgamated in 1948.

Five

Knitting

The Reverend William Lee was responsible for inventing the knitting frame in 1589. It is said that he had observed his wife labouriously hand knitting and believed there was a way to improve the process.

Macclesfield is not traditionally associated with knitting, the process being more associated with the East Midlands, particularly Nottingham and Leicester. Knitted silk and rayon fabrics were, however, manufactured in Macclesfield by a number of firms, particularly at the beginning of the century. Frames of the type developed by William Lee with the bearded needle were in use for the production of scarves and ties by a number of firms. Cartwright and Sheldon, for example, had a number of frames and brought knitters from the East Midlands to operate them. Circular knitting frames using the latch needle were a later invention, and this type of machine was adapted to belt drive mechanism, whereas the early flat bed machines were hand operated. The circular bed machines manufactured items like scarves and ties, but were also used to produce wide fabrics as a tube, which were made up into garments. Today Lomas, W K Lowe and Umbro operate computerised knitting machinery.

Illustration of a hand frame knitter using a flat bed hand frame taken from Diderot's Encyclopaedia.

Charles Mason hand frame knitting at Paradise Mill c. 1950. Cartwright & Sheldon brought hand frame knitters to Macclesfield from Nottingham in the 1920s and established a thriving knitting section. A restored hand frame can be seen in the Paradise Mill Silk Museum.

Above: Here Charles Mason can be seen producing a row of knitted ties which were popular in the 1920s. Hand frame knitted evening scarves were another favourite product. In addition to plain white evening scarves a wide variety of multi-coloured designs were produced for day wear.

Right: An advertisement for a selection of hand frame knitted artificial silk scarves manufactured by Cartwright and Sheldon. In a table drawn up by the Macclesfield Silk Trade Employers Association in about 1929, eleven manufacturers are listed as engaged in knitted fabric or garment production.

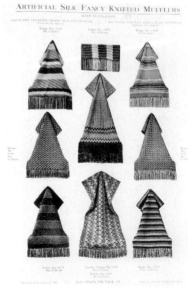

ARTIFICIAL SILK FANCY KNITTED MUFFLERS

Tubular knitting at Neckwear Ltd c. 1957 in the Grosvenor St Mill. Knitted fabric for making up garments was often made in a tubular form before being opened up by cutting.

Above: Tubular knitting machines in Grosvenor St Mill. The complex of mills known as the Grosvenor Street Mills developed over a period of time from 1814 and was used for a variety of silk processes until 1960.

Right: Advertisement from the official Guide to Macclesfield 1951. Neckwear Ltd was established as a fabric and garment manufacturer in 1909.

An example of Quality Knitwear entirely produced in MACCLESFIELD by skilled Craftspeople

in the Grosvenor St. Mills of NECKWEAR Ltd

W K Lowe & Co Ltd, established in 1947, is now the largest garment manufacturer in Macclesfield. Using computer controlled knitting machines they produces jersey fabrics.

Six

Dyeing and Printing

Macclesfield has been associated with dyeing and printing since the early 19th century and the dyeing industry developed to meet the needs of the silk industry. Some silk manufacturers, such as James Arnold & Co, had their own dyehouses which existed in the town alongside specialist dyeing firms. As the man-made fibre industry developed in the 20th century, so the dyehouses and dyeworks adapted accordingly.

The most significant printing firm in the area was founded by William Smith at Langley in 1820. It passed through the family to William Whiston and in 1929 amalgamated with J & T Brocklehurst to form the formidable Brocklehurst Whiston Amalgamated. The early commercial processes included hand tyeing and dyeing, wax resist printing using indigo, and copper plate printing. By the end of the 19th century the firm had the largest collection of hand blocks in Europe and printed fabrics for markets worldwide. With its own block engraving shop many blocks were produced on the premises.

Hand screen printing introduced in both Langley and at Barracks Printing Co in the 1920s proved to be a cheaper and quicker alternative to hand block printing. With the mechanisation of screen printing, hand block printing gradually died out. Both firms proved to be innovative, trying new techniques and adapting to new fibres. The Barracks Printing Co, now part of the Courtaulds Group, today specialises in commission work printing short high quality runs using acid, pigment reactive and vat dyestuffs.

Hand block printer from The Book of Trades c. 1840

The Waller Street dyeworks were occupied from about 1870 by the Abraham family. Thomas Abraham began dyeing silk in 1840 in Rainow; John and David Abraham carried on the business which expanded rapidly. The site continued to be used for dyeing until about 1960. The single storey shown here has the typical louvred ventilation.

The Park Green dyeworks was situated along the River Bollin between Brook Street and the Methodist Chapel on Park Green. The original dyeworks was built about 1809 but was replaced in the 20th century by more modern buildings. The Bollin was regularly polluted by dyestuffs from the mills.

Amalgamated Society of Dyers Certificate presented to Adrian Ashness in 1895.

The skeins of silk were washed in vats to remove impurities at James Arnold's London Road dyeworks in the 1930s.

After washing, the skeins were hung on lines to dry at James Arnold's London Road dyeworks in the 1930s.

The hanks of silk were dipped in vast tubs of dye at the London Road dyeworks owned by J Arnold & Co.

James Arnold & Co purchased the London Road Dyeworks in 1920. In the photograph the dyed hanks are being rewound after the dyeing process is completed.

Above: The Block Engraving shop at Brocklehurst Whiston Amalgamated, Langley, in 1948. Each block engraver made his own tools during his apprenticeship. These were kept in a purpose built cabinet which on retirement was often passed to a colleague or family member..

Opposite above: Rope dyeing is a process by which the woven cloth is wound into ropes for dyeing in the piece. The fabric is lowered into the dye vats across a beam. This photograph was taken at B.W.A. in the 1940s.

Opposite below: Shrigley Dyers was established in 1937 when the firm processed silk and wool for scarves. Today a variety of fabrics are dyed and finished.

THE AMALGAMATED SOCIETY OF

PRINT BLOCK, ROLLER, AND STAMP CUTTERS

EST. 1891

AND DRAUGHTSMEN

AFFILIATED TO THE GENERAL FEDERATION OF TRADE UNIONS

WALLPAPERS
STAMPS
LINOLEUM
BOX-LININGS

CALICO
CRETONNES
SILKS
FABRICS

This is to Certify

that Mr *C. H. Dawson*

has served his Apprenticeship as a *Type Burner & Caster*

to the satisfaction of, in accordance with, the Rules and
Regulations of the above Society.

Signed *Thomas C. Allerton* Gen. Secretary

George Love President

Clifford Howe Treasurer

Above: A seven year apprenticeship was served for both block making and block printing. This
certificate was awarded to Cyril Dawson who served his apprenticeship as a type burner and
caster. He spent all his working life at the Langley Print Works. .

Opposite above: Peter Hammond is making a corner block of pre-cast designs. Note the border
designs and paisley motifs. The corner block would be printed in rotation to create the complete
design for a silk square.

Opposite below: Arthur Pickford, also working at Langley in 1948, is burning a motif into the end
grain of lime wood to create the mould for casting. Molten metal is then poured into the mould.
When the required number of metal castings have been produced they are arranged and fixed
onto the wooden block. The metal castings create the printing surface of
the block.

F Wilson, a Langley printer, is seen here preparing the table to take the fabric ready for block printing. The fabric is lightly stuck down to the table to ensure the cloth does not move during printing.

E Simpson printing on one of the long expanses of table. The tierer's trolley which held the colour is clearly visible and in the background printed fabric hangs up to dry.

Above: W Bailey lays the allover design block on the fabric. The mallet, known as the 'maul', is used to give extra pressure. Note that it is the handle which makes contact with the block, not the head as you might think.

Right: The Printing Block Store at Langley. A small section of the 90,000 blocks which made it the largest collection of printing blocks in Europe. When the department closed most of the blocks were burnt and only a small number of complete sets remain. The majority of these are now in the collections of the Zucchi Textile firm at Ossona near Milan.

William Bailey, a block printer at Langley in 1948 wearing the printer's apron traditionally known as a 'brat'. Note the pattern reference number on the side of the block. The registration pins at each corner of the block ensure the correct position of the blocks as each colour is applied. Five to seven blocks would usually be required for a completed pattern.

The block printing department of James Arnold & Co in 1933.

F Morris and F MacKinstrey in the steam room at Langley in 1948. The colours of the designs are set by steam.

Above: Miss E Sutton at BWA Langley Print Works in 1948 preparing the silk for the tie and dye process. This process was introduced to Langley in the 1820s by William Smith. The effect was replicated in the mid 20th century by printing techniques but is more traditionally associated with Indian and Indonesian fabrics.

Opposite above: Silk screen printers at Park Adam Print Works, Langley. The two printers would practice the technique for handing over the 'squeegee' to ensure the even pressure of the rubber blade which squeezed ink through the screen mesh onto the fabric. The even pressure was essential to create an even distribution of the ink on the cloth.

Opposite below: Handscreen printing at Brocklehurst Whiston Amalgamated in the 1940s. A closer view of O Proudlove and G Bailey passing the 'squeegee' from one to the other. Rows of fabric can be seen hanging up to dry.

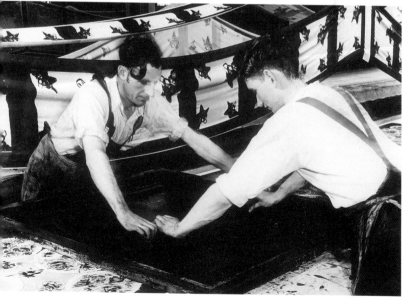

Above: Stentering at Brocklehurst Whiston Amalgamated in 1948. After printing, the fabric is straightened and stretched to the required width. The selvedges are attached to a series of pins as the fabric is fed through the stenter.

Left: Adamley Textiles was established in 1965 as a hand block printing business; block printing was gradually superceded by screen printing. Screens must be thoroughly cleaned after every print, hence the pressure hoses at Park Adam in 1986.

Seven

Products and Making Up

In the 17th and 18th century Macclesfield was known for the production of buttons made from silk and mohair twist. After broadloom weaving was introduced towards the end of the 18th century the main products were calgees and bandanna handkerchiefs. At the Great Exhibition of 1851 Macclesfield firms exhibited a wide variety of high quality products including sarsenets, vestings, handkerchiefs, velvets, satins, ribbons and shawls. By 1895, at an exhibition to mark the Duchess of Teck's visit to the town, products included a variety of dress fabrics, shawls, handkerchiefs, mufflers and ties. Admiralty contracts for black squares were substantial business for many firms.

In the 20th century the manufacture of tie material took an increasingly important role. Cartwright and Sheldon, founded in 1912, specialised in high quality 28" handloom woven squares. Other firms wove 24" cut ups for the cheaper end of the market. Macclesfield became well known for its 'neat' designs and 'steels' which are still worn today for formal occasions.

Many firms had large knitting and making up departments, using man-made fibres alongside silk. In the 1920s and 1930s Macclesfield boiling silk with a spun silk warp and crepe weft made its mark. Striped patterns were particularly popular. Printed silk and rayon handkerchiefs and bias crepe scarves were other products of this period.

In World War II local firms contributed to the war effort, in particular weaving silk for parachutes. In the latter half of the 20th century the manufacture of club tie material became the main product. Today those firms still in business in the town specialise in the club tie trade as well as weaving and printing fashion fabrics for both home and abroad.

Macclesfield's silk manufacturers diversified into making up when the silk trade experienced slumps in the 19th century.

The Duchess of Teck, who was patron of the British silk industry and President of the Ladies Section of the Silk Association of Great Britain, visited Macclesfield in 1895. An exhibition was held at the School of Art at which local manufacturers demonstrated the range of their products.

The making up department of James Kershaw preserved at Bond St Mill c. 1900. Kershaw's produced a wide range of silk goods including jacquard tie cloth, mufflers and ladieswear. There were two machine rooms making blouses and babywear.

FOR HOLIDAY WEAR

FOR the latest styles in Costumes, Blouse-Robes, Frocks, Blouses, etc., send to-day for a *free* copy of our "ILLUSTRATED CATALOGUE OF FASHIONS."

FOR HOME-DRESSMAKING

Send for full collection of patterns of Dress Material, Silks, Blouse Fabrics, etc. Endless variety.

Illustrated in the Catalogue will be found all the newest styles and designs, which will enable you to choose your new clothes at home in comfort, and at prices to suit all needs. Illustrations of Models 161 and 164 are examples of the value we offer. Fit, style and finish unequalled.

Smart and attractive Styles in VOILE.

DRESS MATERIALS

include latest productions, prices from 2/6 to 15/6 per yard.

SILKS in the loveliest colourings and designs, prices from 2/6 to 17/6 per yard.

BLOUSE FABRICS

in great variety, prices from 9½d. to 4/6 per yard.

Patterns sent post free on approval.

Model 161

Very charming Model of fine White Voile, cut on the very newest lines in the deep-waisted effect and tunic of lovely Swiss embroidery and Val. lace.

39/6
Carr. Paid.

All orders sent Carriage Paid in United Kingdom. Satisfaction guaranteed or money refunded.

Model 164

Extremely neat and Becoming Dress of fine White Voile. Cut with the fashionable oval collar and dainty Swiss embroidered panel front, inset with hemstitching.

25/9
Car.pd.

ROBINSON BROWN
(Dept. 6), MACCLESFIELD.

Robinson Brown advertisement c. 1914. This company offered a mail order service of ready-to-wear garments. Customers could also visit the Royal Silk Warehouse on Waters Green (now Clowes Printing Works) to select their patterns and fabric.

At the British Scientific Products Exhibition held in London in September 1918, James Arnold exhibited a wide range of products. Many Macclesfield firms had London agents or offices to promote their goods.

Invoice heading for Robinson Brown in 1905 showing the Royal Silk Warehouse which was built in 1903. It is the only retail warehouse known to have been built specifically for the sale of manufactured silk goods in Macclesfield.

Right: Inspecting the finished cloth and removing ends from the length of silk brocade woven by B. W. A and presented by Macclesfield Borough Council as a wedding gift to Princess Elizabeth in 1947

Below: Quality control. Using pickers to remove loose ends from a piece of Macclesfield silk stripe at Brocklehurst Whiston Amalgamated in the 1940s.

Making Up Department at Cartwright and Sheldon in 1933. Mrs Gertrude Snodin (in striped top) cutting out printed bias scarves ready for hemming. The majority of the printing for Cartwright and Sheldon was undertaken by Barrack's Printing Co.

Another photograph from Cartwright and Sheldon in 1933 showing biased scarves in the making up department. Scarves in both silk and rayon were popular in the 1920s and 1930s. Weaving firms developed making up as a substantial subsidiary business which helped to diversify their business particularly when the market for woven goods was poor. Cartwright and Sheldon produced neckwear and handkerchiefs.

. . . . . IN GREAT AND
INCREASING DEMAND

"Maccleboil" Pure Silk
Handkerchiefs and Scarves
are an essential accessory to
the smart woman's toilet.
They add the final touch of
colourful chic to the season's
smartest frocks and costumes.
All the vivid colours woven
into the rich pure silk are
guaranteed fast boiling.

Exclusively through the Wholesale & Shipping

"MACCLEBOIL"

**Pure Silk
HANDKERCHIEFS
AND SCARVES**

Sole Manufacturers:
DAVID WHITFIELD & Co. Ltd.
WATERSIDE MILLS
MACCLESFIELD

BRITISH MADE

PURE SILK CREPE
FAST
BOILING COLS.
MACCLEBOIL
REG^D
WOVEN IN
MACCLESFIELD ENG.

Peter Robinson catalogue 1933. 'Maccleboil' was the trademark of David Whitfield who first
introduced spun crepe washing silk. Other Macclesfield firms wove checked, striped and
plain fabrics in spun crepe marketed it under names such as 'Duboil' and 'Ucanboil'. The
fabric was hardwearing with excellent washing properties and colour fast when boiled making
it excellent for everyday wear, nightwear and sports clothes.

Joseph Dunkerley & Son, 1933. Forty machinists were employed in the making up section. Many of the girls can be seen wearing Macclesfield striped dresses.

Joseph Dunkerley & Son 1933. Madge Dunkerley managed the making up department which employed about 60 girls altogether. She adapted Paris fashions for the ready to wear market producing garments for private customers and retailers like John Lewis and Harrods. A distinctive Macclesfield stripe is laid out in the foreground, ready for cutting.

Above: Leodian catalogue c. 1935. Leodian was a Leeds based company which offered a mail order service for dresses made from Macclesfield silk. A range of styles and qualities was presented from which the customer could choose.

Above: Advertisement for Harry Turner (Macclesfield) Ltd from the Silk Journal and Rayon World 1933-43

Left: Advertisement for Macclesfield Silk Stripe Blouse c. 1930.

With a Satin Stripe.
A new washing silk shirting is used for this neat short-sleeved style with pointed yoke at back and short revers. In ivory/red, ivory/blue and ivory/navy.
Sizes 13—14½ .. **39/6**

Sent on Approval

Joseph Dunkerley & Son 1933. Making up and packaging handkerchiefs at the Oxford Road mill. The trade name 'New Oxford' appears on the corner of the spun crepe handkerchiefs. Another trade name was 'Sylqueena' - appropriate as the firm was an enthusiastic supporter of the annual 'Silk Queen' competition.

Working conditions in the making up department of Brocklehurst Whiston Amalgamated appear to have been very cramped in 1933.

Packaging of made up goods was an important part of marketing in the 1930s as it is today. Most firms had their own packaging departments.

Cartwright and Sheldon exhibited at the Wembley Exhibition in 1924. The items shown here demonstrate a wide range of knitted and woven products. Samples of the woven silks exhibited and other products are now in the Museum collections. Exhibiting at major trade fairs was an important part of marketing activity.

Above: Advertisement for artificial silk stockings from the Silk Journal & Rayon World 1925.

Left: Advertisement from the Silk Journal 1933.

Eight

Education and Training

Elementary education in Macclesfield was available for those who could afford it from 1498, when the Grammar School was founded by Sir John Percival. The first formal education, for those who did not have the financial resources to pay, was provided by the Sunday School movement. The Macclesfield Sunday School Trust was founded in 1796 and the large Sunday School building was erected between 1813-1814. The National School was built on Duke Street in 1813 and was the response of the Anglican Church to the non-denominational nature of the large Sunday School.

The first state education was provided as a result of the 1870 Education Act. This led to a large number of schools providing free education for children without financial resources. Child labour was common in the silk industry as it was in other industries in the 19th and early 20th centuries. Training for the industry was mainly done on the job, but the industrial school provided specific training for employment.

Specialist skills for the silk industry were acquired at the Art School or the Technical School, which were built in the second half of the 19th century with the encouragement of government grants. Attendance at night school or day release was expected as part of the apprenticeship system. The School of Art enjoyed a good reputation for the quality of its teachers and the students it produced were to contribute to the development of the silk industry nationally. However, students today have to travel further afield to fulfil the training needs of the industry.

Children received formal education at Sunday Schools prior to the 1870 Education Act which provided free state education

Above: The Sunday School movement in Macclesfield was founded by John Whitaker in 1796. In 1813 money was raised by voluntary donations for a purpose built non-denominational Sunday School on Roe Street. The building, which cost £5,600, held 2,500 children, the majority of whom worked in the mills six days a week. Macclesfield Sunday School became the centre for religious education and social life in the town. In addition to providing religious instruction and formal education it offered a programme of social events both in the evening and at weekends.

Opposite: Illustrated talks were featured in the programme; the one advertised in the poster was clearly intended to be educational as well as entertaining since it records the journey of Stanley in a series of coloured views, which were shown in the large room of the Sunday School with the aid of an oxy-hydrogen lime light.

MACCLESFIELD
SUNDAY SCHOOL

STANLEY
IN AFRICA

ILLUSTRATED BY THE AID OF THE OXY-HYDROGEN LIME LIGHT

WITH

OVER 40 COLOURED VIEWS !

From the Commencement of his Expedition to Central Africa to his Return to England, and Marriage to Miss Dorothy Tennent, at Westminster Abbey,

TO CONCLUDE

With a Number of Amusing Views

WILL BE GIVEN IN THE

LARGE ROOM OF THE ABOVE SCHOOL

—— ON ——

WEDNESDAY, NOV. 19, 1890

Chair to be taken by **Mr. W. B. STAGHALL.**

DOORS OPEN AT 7, TO COMMENCE AT 7-30.

TICKETS : Reserved Seats, 6d. ; Second Seats, 3d. ; Gallery, 2d.

May be had from the Committee, Teachers, or at the Printer's

Macclesfield **Sunday School**

TEA PARTY

AND ENTERTAINMENT,

TUESDAY, JANUARY 1st, 1895.

SPECIAL ENGAGEMENT OF

Mr. FELIX MILLS, OF OLDHAM

THE CELEBRATED HUMORIST AND ELOCUTIONIST.

An Interesting Fanciful

OPERETTA - - "JACK FROST,"

Will be given by a Children's Choir of 50 voices.—JACK FROST,—Miss S. E. Barber.

Accompanists: Miss Mellor & Miss Pownall, (Cert.) T.C.L. | Mr. D. S. Bowers will conduct the singing.

His Worship the Mayor (Alderman T. Pickford) will preside.

PROGRAMME, PART FIRST.

OPENING HYMN	"The Stately Homes of England," (Tune,—*Partant Pour La Syria*.)	The Audience
	CHAIRMAN'S ADDRESS.	
SONG	"Off to Philadelphia,"	Mr. A. Jones
OPERETTA	"JACK FROST,"	CHILDREN'S CHOIR
CORNET SOLO		Mr. F. Murray
PART SONG	"Let the hills resound," *Brinley Richards*,	The Choir
HUMOROUS SONG	"A Recipe for Comic Songs," *Grain*...	
DIALECT SKETCH	"Fault Finders," *Hartley*...	Mr.
DOMESTIC HUMOUR	"A Parental Ode to my Son, (Aged 3 Years)," *Hood*...	Felix Mills.
NEW MUSICAL SKETCH	"The Seaside Serenaders,"	

Introducing—"The Italian Comic Song,"—(*Lurci*)—Popular Parodies,—The Old Trombone" (*Grain*) And an Extraordinary Combination of Musical Nursery Rhymes.

INTERVAL OF 10 MINUTES.

PART SECOND.

HYMN	"To the Work, to the Work,"—Sankey, No. 176.	The Audience
CORNET SOLO		Mr. F. Murray
DIALOGUE	"The Age of Puffing,"	Five Characters
SONG	"The Jolly Young Waterman,"	Mr. A. Jones
PART SONG	"The Song of the New Year," *Donizetti*,	The Choir
PIANOFORTE SOLO	"Overture," *Rossini*...	Miss Ethel Argyle
HUMOROUS SCENA	"A Rural Railroad Ride," *West*	Mr.
WHISTLING SKETCH	"An Adventure up the Rigi,"	Felix Mills.
MUSICAL SKETCH	"A Juvenile Party," *Grönwill*.	

Introducing—The Invitation,—A Spoiled Coat,—A New Watch,—Two Spoons,— An Indigestible Bun,—A Little Girl Sings "Oh, would I were a Little Bird,"— A Reciter interrupted by a Street Organ,—The Terrible Charges of "The Light Brigade,"—A Wooden Board,—Reminiscence of a Bill-Poster,—Johnsons' Vocal Mixtures.

TEA ON THE TABLES AT FIVE O'CLOCK PROMPT.

TICKETS - ONE SHILLING EACH.

May be had from Mr. Stagholl, Mill Street; Mr. Tatton, Mill Street; Mr. Pownall, Brown Street; Mr. Turner, Mill Lane; Mr. G. D. Cope, Commercial Road; Mr. Barber, Secretary, 27, Buckley Street; or from any of the Teachers.

W. COLLINS, PRINTER AND BOOKBINDER, PARK GREEN, MACCLESFIELD.

The Sunday School was also responsible for organising excursions and teas from time to time. The tea party organised for New Year's Day 1895 was a significant event with tickets costing one shilling (5p) each and tea to be served at five o'clock prompt. Entertainment was likely to be a mixture of in-house activities with participation from the children of the school and special guest performers.

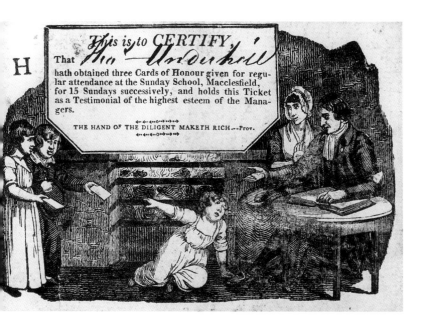

H

This is to CERTIFY,
That *Mrs Underhill*
hath obtained three Cards of Honour given for regular attendance at the Sunday School, Macclesfield,
for 15 Sundays successively, and holds this Ticket
as a Testimonial of the highest esteem of the Mana-
gers.

THE HAND OF THE DILIGENT MAKETH RICH.—Prov.

Above: Discipline was strict. Children who attended punctually for five weeks were given Honours Cards; when three such cards had been collected they received a certificate.

Right: The Sunday School Beadle, known as the nobbler, John Henry Lomas c. 1900.

Above: The National School in Duke Street was built in 1813 as the first elementary day school in Macclesfield and as a Sunday School associated with the Church of England. It remained in use until 1960.

Opposite: Poster of 1842 advertising the annual sermon, which was a major fund raising event for both the National School and the Large Sunday School.

V. R.

NATIONAL DAY SCHOOL,

MACCLESFIELD.

ON SUNDAY, JUNE 12, 1842,

THE ANNUAL

SERMON

WILL BE PREACHED IN THE

OLD CHURCH,

BY THE

REV. J. B. SWEET,

M.A., AND A COLLECTION MADE IN SUPPORT OF

THE NATIONAL DAY SCHOOL.

A SELECTION OF SACRED MUSIC WILL BE GIVEN.

The Choir will be assisted by the Macclesfield Choral Society.—Mr Mason will preside at the Organ.

SERVICE TO COMMENCE AT THREE O'CLOCK.

SILVER WILL, AS IS USUAL, BE RECEIVED AT THE DOORS.

NUMBER OF CHILDREN—BOYS, 130, GIRLS, 117. TOTAL, 247.

J. SWINNERTON, PRINTER, MACCLESFIELD.

The Industrial School c. 1905, also known as the Macclesfield Ragged School, was founded in 1858 for vagrant, orphaned and neglected children. They were taught to read and write and given a daily meal. Those over eight years were apprenticed in the silk mills and proved willing pupils. In 1866 a new school with living accommodation and recreational facilities was erected on Brook Street.

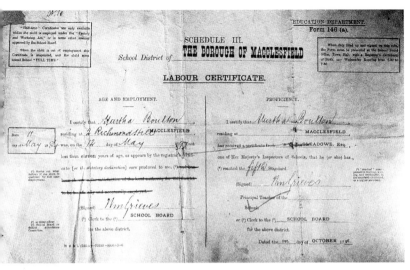

Labour certificate for Martha Boulton 1897. In 1875 the Factory Act made 10 years the minimum age for half-time employment on the production of an exemption certificate. Full time employment could begin at 13. After 1918 it was compulsory to attend full time education between 5 and 14.

Class of boys c. 1900 who have obviously been told to come in their Sunday best. Classes were often taught by pupil-teachers.

Great Choral Concert.

MACCLESFIELD SOCIETY FOR ACQUIRING USEFUL KNOWLEDGE.

THE SECOND ANNUAL CHORAL CON-CERT will be held, by permission of the Ma-nagers, at the MACCLESFIELD SUNDAY SCHOOL, on THURSDAY Evening, Jan. 2, 1840.

PRINCIPAL PERFORMERS.

MISS LEACH,

(Of the Manchester and Liverpool Concerts.)

Leader, Mr. BARNES, (of the Manchester Concerts.)

PRINCIPAL TRUMPET,

Mr. BANKS, (of the same Concerts.)

Double Drums—J. LEACH, Esq., of Stockport.

Conductor, Mr. Mason.

Mr. TWISS will preside at the Organ.

The BAND and CHORUS will be on an extensive scale, and complete in every department,

CONSISTING OF NEARLY

One Hundred & Fifty Performers.

Above: The Useful Knowledge Society formed in the 1830s, moved to the former Parsonage Building on Park Green in 1850. Its original aim was to supply instruction in the three Rs to the young men of Macclesfield. The Art School and Technical School both developed from the work of the Society.

Left: The annual choral concert became a significant fund raising event for the Useful Knowledge Society, which relied on public support to sustain its operation.

Opposite above: The Useful Knowledge Society founded the School of Design above its Park Green premises in 1852. By 1879 the School of Art and Design, as it was then called, had moved to Park Lane. The school gained a high reputation and students contributed to design both in Macclesfield and further afield.

The Technical School also emanated from the Useful Knowledge Society and was closely associated with the School of Art. Students went to the Art School for weaving but to the Technical School for throwing. Local firms and manufacturers donated the machinery used by the students. The Ruti Company of Switzerland were among those who donated looms.

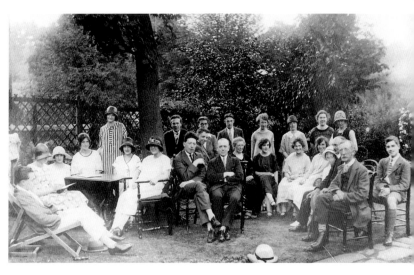

Above: Thomas Cartwright (front right of group) was head of the Art School from 1907 until 1927. Here is a sketching party led by him in the 1920s with Charles Tunnicliffe, the well known bird artist, sitting centre left.

Left: James Ward was appointed head of the School of Art in 1888. During his period it was one of the country's leading art schools. In 1907 he took up a position in Dublin.

Nine

Leisure and Recreation

Leisure and recreation for the working population during the early 19th century was largely confined to Sundays, since the long hours left little time for recreational activity during the working week.

The campaign for public open spaces began in the 1830s and the first public park to open in Macclesfield was West Park in 1854, which was funded by public contributions. Parks in urban centres like Manchester had appeared a decade earlier but the pressures and lack of proximity to the open countryside were probably greater in the city centre than in Macclesfield. Other Macclesfield parks were to follow: Victoria Park in 1894 and South Park in 1922. The parks provided pleasant open space with facilities for outdoor recreational activities such as bowling. Each park also had a bandstand where musical performances were staged for the entertainment of local people.

The silk industry, like many other industries, had fixed holidays with Barnaby in June and Wakes in October. The carnival was a major event in the town which was held close to Barnaby. Many of the local community group and silk manufacturing firms produced elaborate floats for the event and marching bands accompanied the procession. From the 1930s the Silk Queen was a feature at the carnival and local social and civic events.

Other forms of entertainment and recreation were offered by the churches which, together with the workplace, was the major focus for social activity. Churches and Sunday Schools had sports teams and organised social events and entertainment. The large Sunday School became the focus for a wide range of social, sporting, educational and religious activities.

For the working population leisure time was very limited and children made use of any open space to pursue games and leisure pursuits.

Above: The Heatherbells Jazz Band was made up of staff and their families from G H Heath, Silk Throwsters. The band is seen here playing kazoos in the Macclesfield Carnival of 1933.

Left: Cartoon from Macarag the carnival programme.

The Man who asked for change at the Macclesfield Carnival!

The band from Messrs H Turner Ltd Silk Manufacturers was known as Appy Ambone. Choosing a catchy name was all important to the image of the band. Harry Turner left a legacy 'to provide dwelling for impoverished textile silk workers'. The houses near Ryles Park are now tenanted by ex-silk workers of 'good character'.

Wm Frost & Sons of Park Green Mill were obviously very proud of their band, known as Silk Town's Prize Jazz Band. It was made up of employees and their relatives. The girls are distinctive in Macclesfield stripe.

The Large Sunday School was the venue for a wide range of musical entertainment in the early part of the 20th century. Mr Loose (standing back left on lower image) organised many events which were very popular.

Macclesfield's first Rose Queen - Miss Dorothy Cooper in 1913. Like other towns Macclesfield selected or elected a Rose Queen.

Miss Lilian Jervis travelled Britain extensively as Macclesfield's first Silk Queen. She was inaugurated in 1930 amid great publicity, promoting both the town and the industry.

Above: Miss Lilian Jervis [later Mrs Lilian Dale] seen here at a Civic reception with the Mayor of South Shields in 1930. She worked for Madge Dunkerley, of Joseph Dunkerley. The firm produced a silk handkerchief bearing her portrait to commemorate her year as Silk Queen, and clearly they saw the commercial benefits of organising and promoting the Silk Queen as part of their business activities.

Right: Emmie Plant, the Silk Queen of 1934 in full regalia. The Lancashire towns had Cotton Queens during the same period.

Victoria Park bandstand 1894. Bandstands provided a focal point with regular musical entertainment. Visitors could either sit and listen to the music or dance on the specially asphalted areas which surrounded the bandstand.

Victoria Park was donated to Macclesfield by Francis Dicken Brocklehurst of the silk manufacturing firm and opened in 1894 amidst great celebration. It was named after the Queen at the request of the donor and occupies land on which the Brocklehurst's family home "The Fence" once stood. This view, taken in about 1900, shows the popularity of the wide open spaces in the parks for recreation.

Macclesfield Infirmary was built through the perseverance of John May with an endowment from Joseph Tunnicliffe, a local silk manufacturer, and public subscriptions. When the Infirmary was demolished for the development of Sainsburys supermarket, the time capsule, which had been buried under the foundation stone in 1867, was retrieved. However, its contents were somewhat disappointing since the seal was not airtight and only the coins survived intact.

The rose garden in West Park with the original Pavilion tea rooms designed by A W N Pugin, who also designed St Albans Church. Britain was the first country to develop public parks. Originally parks provided opportunities for rather formal recreation but are now much more informal with a range of activities.

Above: Central Station was opened in
1872 when the Marple to Macclesfield
branch of the Sheffield and
Lincolnshire Railway was finished.
Considerable demolition of property
was required to build the line and
associated buildings.

Left: The first passenger train out of
Macclesfield was on 24 November
1845. The railway companies
promoted excursions and leisure
travel. For the first time the working
classes had the opportunity to travel
at holiday time. Barnaby Sunday is
always between June 19th and 25th
whilst Wakes is the 29th September or
the first Sunday following.

Above: A charabanc outing to Southport by James Arnold's employees. By the 1930s the charabanc began to rival the train as a primary means of conveyance to the seaside. Charabanc outings provided a popular distraction for textile workers particularly at Barnaby Holidays. Note there was little shelter from the weather, although some charabancs offered protection many were open topped.

Right: A humorous postcard of the 1920s recording the role of the 'Knocker Up' who performed a useful role knocking on windows to wake people for work prior to alarm clocks or telephone alarm calls. Strict timekeeping was adhered to and latecomers would be locked out, thus losing a day's pay.

123

Above: In 1936 H G Wells' 'Things to Come' created a great stir, and the associated publicity obviously attracted the interest of the local children of Macclesfield, for whom the cinema was probably the major source of entertainment in the days prior to television.

Left: Moving pictures became a novelty during the last years of the 19th century, featuring on music hall bills and at fairgrounds. Small purpose built cinemas developed during the Edwardian period and by 1926 some 3000 cinemas were in operation. By the 1930s the cinema has become, in A J P Taylor's words, "the essential social habit of the age". There were six cinemas in Macclesfield, the Majestic on Mill Street was built in 1922 and the photograph shows Mrs Elkin at the box office in 1940.

Many of the celebrated British football clubs originated from church, school and working men's teams. The Macclesfield Sunday School organised a wide range of sporting activities, among them the football team pictured here in 1902/03 outside the entrance to the Sunday School building. One imagines the gentlemen standing on the extreme left with the towel over his shoulder must be the coach.

The Hovis Company, established in Macclesfield around the end of the nineteenth and the beginning of the twentieth centuries, had a large workforce and encouraged its employees to play an active role in the community.

Above: The cause for celebration at James Arnold's works recorded in this photograph was the end of the first world war in 1918. Note the combined flag of the allies including the Japanese flag integrated between that of Britain, France, Holland and Belgium and home made banners proclaiming 'Long Live the King' and 'God Bless our Boys'.

Opposite above: National parliamentary elections were of particular interest, especially at Brocklehursts as the family had over the years provided the town with a succession of its Members of Parliament. Here the weaving shed is decorated during election time.

Opposite below: The Coronation of Elizabeth II in 1953 was also the cause for some celebration since, as the Princess Elizabeth, she had paid a visit to the factory some years earlier and been given a length of jacquard woven silk to commemorate the visit.

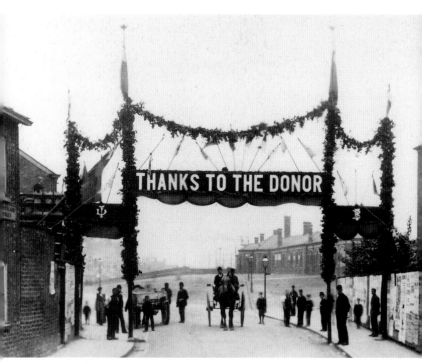

THANKS TO THE DONOR

The silk manufacturers dominated the industrial, political and social life of the town. Whilst they were motivated by profit and hard task masters, their wives and daughters sat on various social and charitable committees. Families, like the Brocklehursts, contributed to the provision of facilities in the town. This photograph shows a banner erected on the opening of Victoria Park which was given to the town by the Brocklehursts in 1894.